T
GUILDHALL

Sound at Sight

piano

Book 1

Published by Trinity College *London*
89 Albert Embankment
London
SE1 7TP, UK

Printed in England by Caligraving Ltd, Thetford, Norfolk

Sound at sight

Playing or singing music that has not been seen before is a necessary part of any musician's life, and the exploration of a new piece should be an enjoyable and stimulating process.

Reading music requires two main things: first, the ability to grasp the meaning of music notation on the page; second, the ability to convert sight into sound and perform the piece. This involves imagining the sound of the music before playing it. This in turn implies familiarity with intervals, chord shapes, rhythmic patterns and textures. The material in this series will help pianists to develop their skills and build confidence.

Plenty of pieces are given throughout, but this is more than just a book of specimen tests. Exercises introduce new skills before they are incorporated in short pieces of music. Guidance is given on the new skills as they are introduced. All this contributes to making this a thoroughly practical course in developing sight reading skills, whether it is used for examination preparation or to increase confidence in the context of solo playing or ensemble work.

Trinity's sight reading requirements are stepped progressively between Initial and Grade 8, with manageable increases in difficulty between each grade. Some tips on examination preparation are given at the back of the book. In all cases, however, references to examination tests are avoided until *after* the relevant material has been practised. This is deliberate: many pupils find the prospect of being tested on sight reading skills to be quite inhibiting at first. The aim is to perform new pieces—the fact that they may be examination tests as well is far less important.

Acknowledgements

Thanks are due to the many composers who have contributed to the series: James Burden, Humphrey Clucas, Colin Cowles, David Dawson, Sébastien Dédis, Peter Fribbins, David Gaukroger, Robin Hagues, Amy Harris, Peter Lawson, Jonathan Paxman, Danielle Perrett and Michael Zev Gordon.

Thanks are also due to Matthew Booth, Luise Horrocks, Geraint John, Joanna Leslie and Anne Smillie for their technical advice.

The *udjat* symbol is an Egyptian hieroglyph called the 'sound eye', and was associated with the god Horus.

• Getting started

Can you name and play these notes? They are all in the five-finger hand position from middle C (C$_4$) in the right hand, and from C$_3$ ('tenor' C) for the left hand.

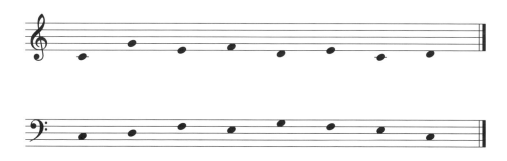

Now try these exercises where the notes are all next-door (adjacent) fingers.

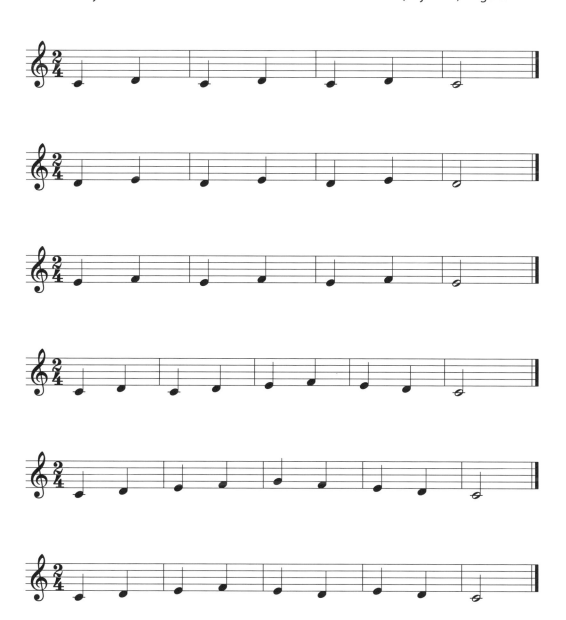

Do not play, but feel the notes under your fingers as you read these leaps: line to a line or space to a space.

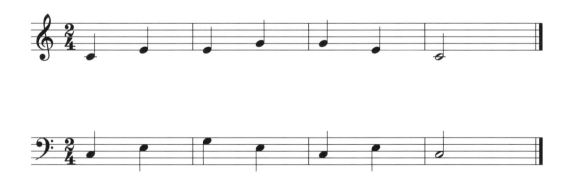

Now put leaps of a third and steps together in these slightly longer examples.

Fourths are a line to a space or a space to a line (fingers 1–4 or 2–5 in the right hand, 2–5 or 1–4 in the left hand). You might like to repeat the first four bars.

Did you notice fifths in these examples?

Can you sing all the exercises so far, out loud or in your head?

Name the notes as you sing and feel the notes under your fingers—but without sounding them. This will be useful preparation for reading pieces later.

• Rhythm and dynamics

You have already seen minims (two-count notes), but now make sure that you count them carefully and hold these notes for their full length.

Now try making notes loud or quiet. Loud is marked f in the music and quiet is marked p.

In this piece, which is shared between the hands, you have to look quickly from one line to the other to see what happens next and whether the note you play should be loud or soft.

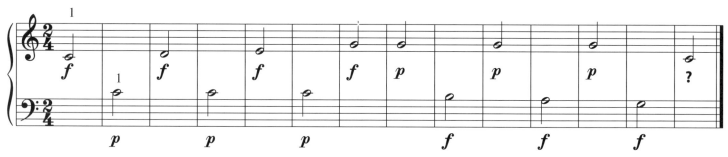

You decide whether the
last note should be f or p

• Pieces for one hand

Now you are ready to play these pieces.

1

2

3

Count four in the next few pieces.

4

5

6

7

● **Melodies for two hands**

Play all these melodies at a comfortable pace (*Moderato*). The sign ▬ is a rest and means that whichever hand has it does not play during these bars. Read each piece through before playing, as you did on page 5.

8

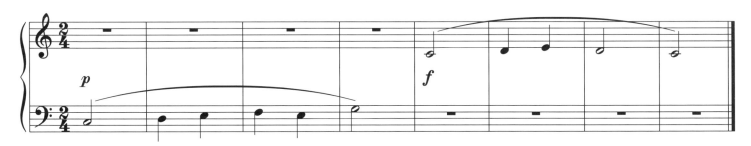

9

10

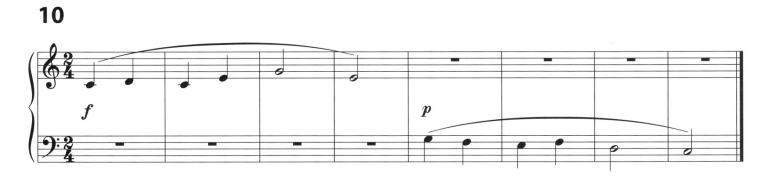

11

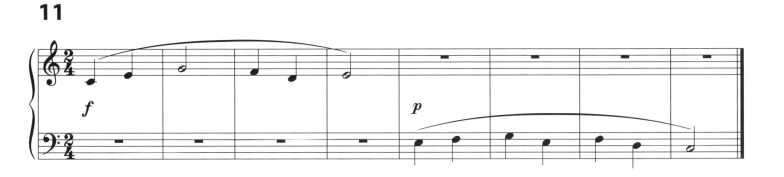

12

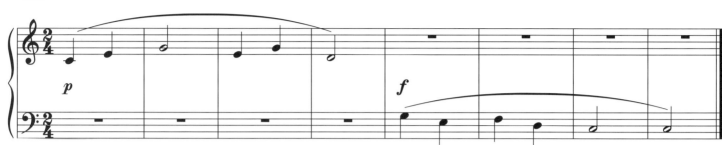

13

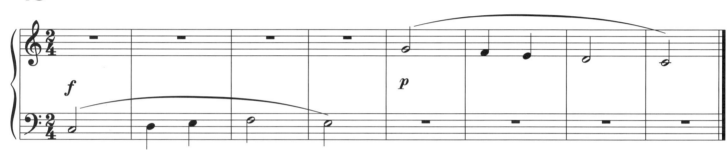

14

15

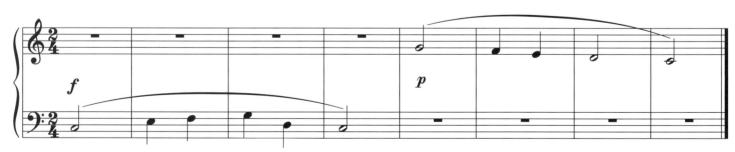

16

17

18

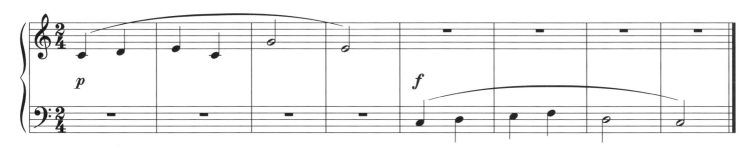

19

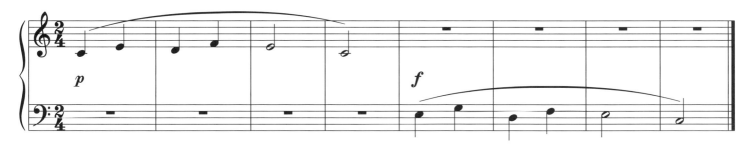

20

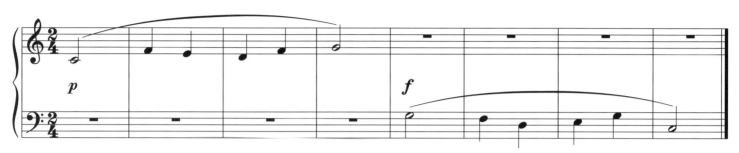

21

22

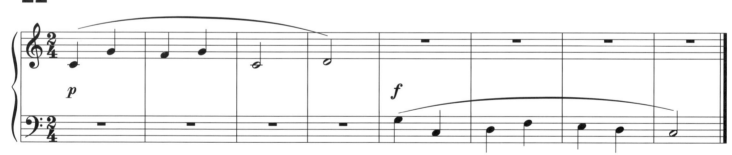

23

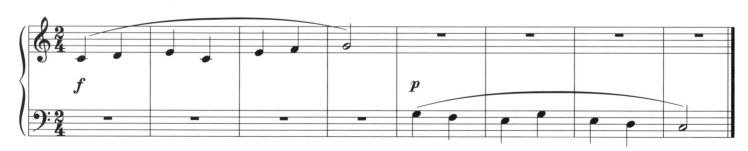

24

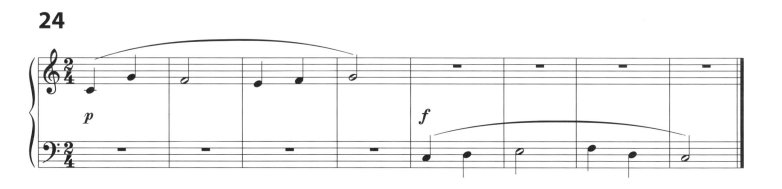

25

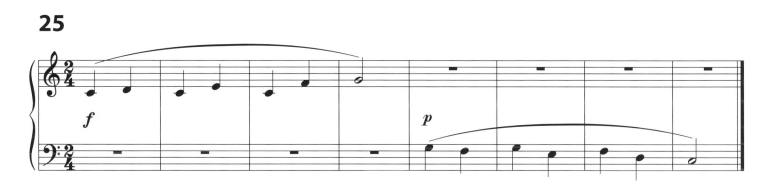

26

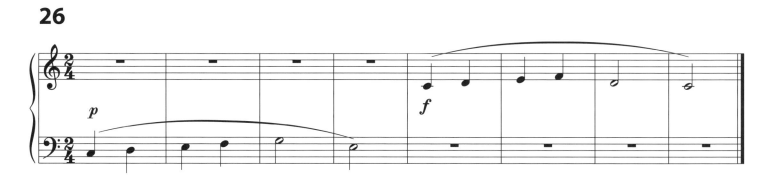

27

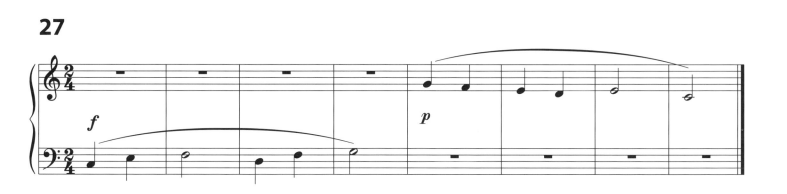

Now try these pieces as if they were examination tests.

28

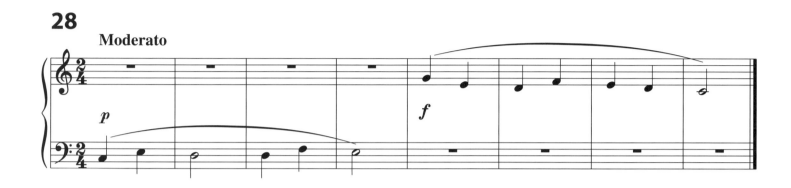

29

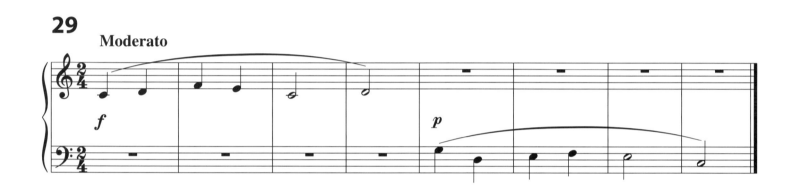

30

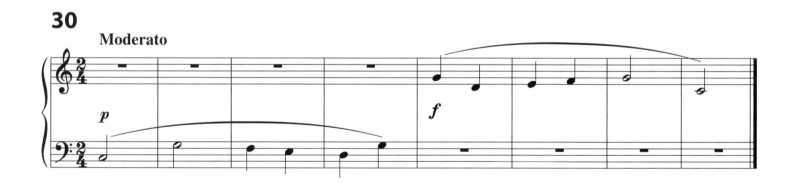

 Melodies 8–30 are of the standard required for Initial grade examinations.

• Two new keys

These melodies are for one hand in a five-finger position, in G major or A minor. Play the chord first and look through the passage, spotting the next-door notes and the leaps. Leave your hand in the chord position as you read through the melody.

31

G major

32

G major

33

A minor

34

A minor

The last note of no. 34 is a semibreve—a four-count note. Make sure that you hold it for its full value. Practise this exercise, starting on the right-hand thumb:

• Hands together

Now try these exercises, where one hand holds a minim and the other plays crotchets (one-count notes) at the same time. Take care to find the correct fingers for the first notes.

Now do the same with semibreves and crotchets:

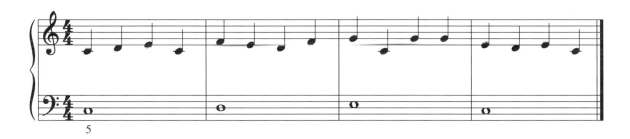

● More on dynamics

You have already played *f* and *p* (loud and quiet). Can you add a step in between? *mf* is moderately loud.

• Melodies for two hands

Play all these melodies at a comfortable pace (*Moderato*). Play the key chord first and keep your hand over the keys as you think through the piece. The hands only play together in the last two bars of these pieces, but keep both hands over the keys ready to play.

Be careful not to let sounds continue into the rests.

35

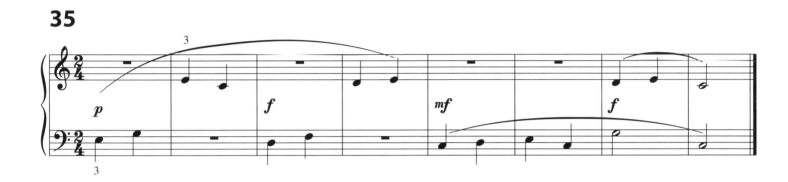

36

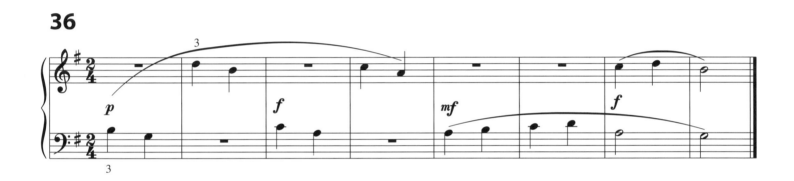

37

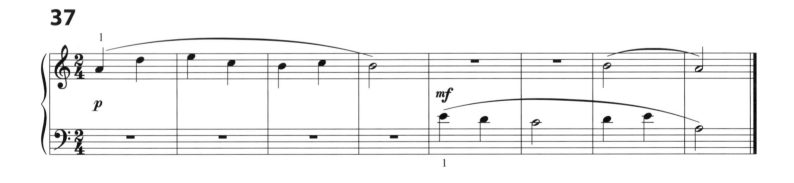

38

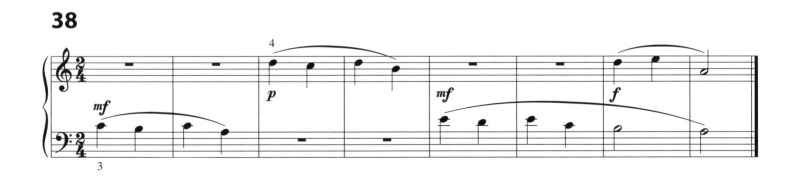

These pieces use the same hand positions you have already learned so no fingering is given, but you will need to check which key you are in.

39

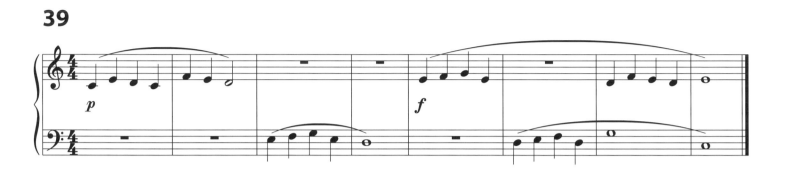

40

41

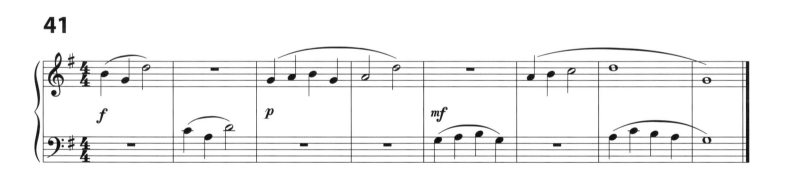

42

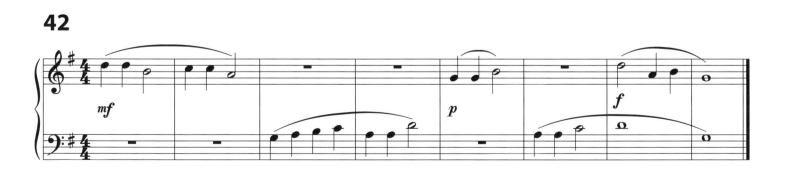

43

44

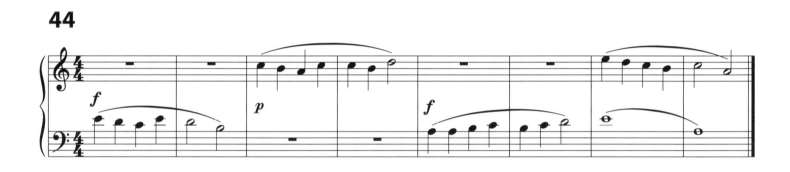

45

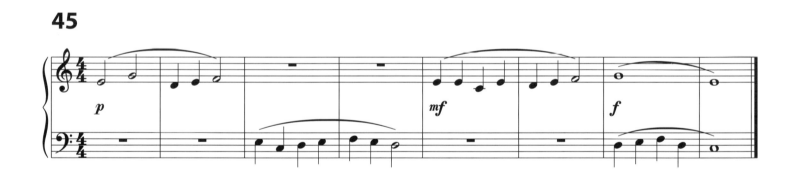

46

47

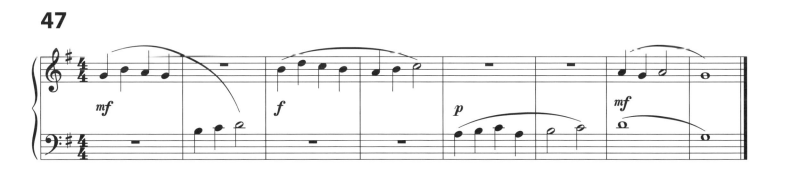

48

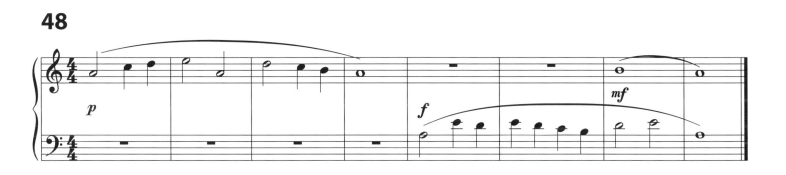

49

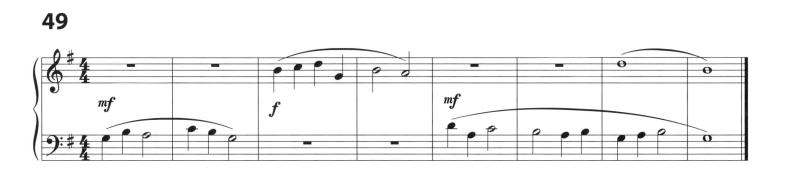

50

51

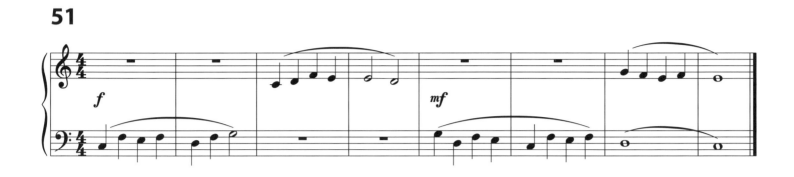

52

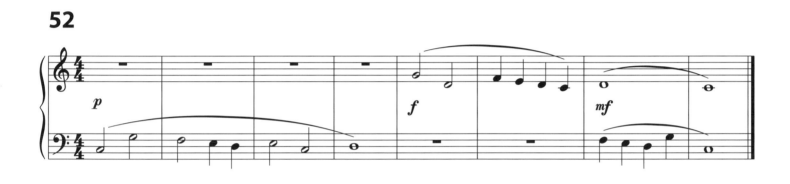

53

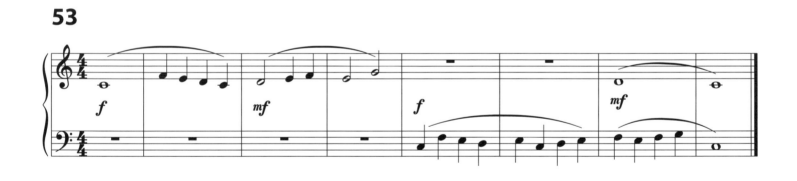

54

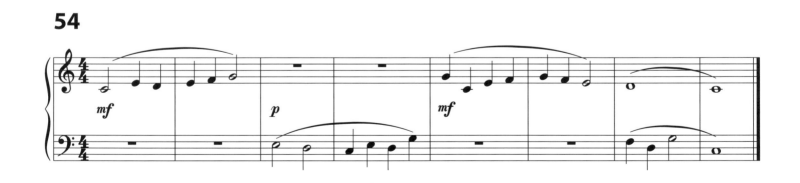

Now try these pieces as if they were examination tests.

55

56

57

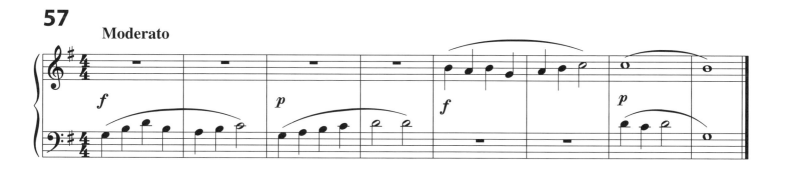

58

 Melodies 39–58 are of the standard required for Grade 1 examinations.

• Ties and dotted notes

You have seen phrasing slurs, which are equivalent to short sentences. A tie looks quite similar but links two identical notes. You do not replay the note but hold it on for the extra value of the second note.

A dot after a note adds half the value of the note: for example, a two-beat note with a dot after it becomes a three-beat note. Always make sure that you give these notes their full value.

A dot after a note adds half the value of the note: for example, a two-beat note with a dot after it becomes a three-beat note. Always make sure that you give these notes their full value.

Watch out for ties and dotted notes in the next two pieces. There is more playing together in these pieces than in previous ones too. *Allegretto* is quite fast so do not play too slowly!

59
Moderato

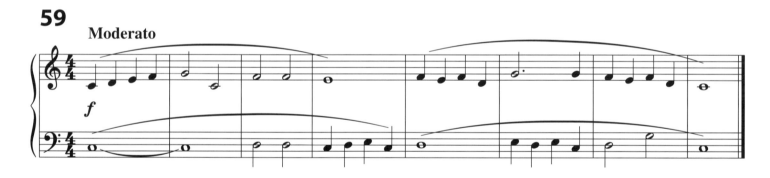

60
Allegretto

• A new time signature

You need to be able to count three beats in the bar now. Notice the dotted minims in the left-hand: they are held for three beats. As you play these exercises, you may find the first beat of the bar benefits from some gentle accentuation.

61 Allegretto

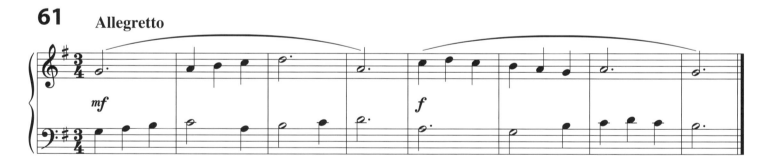

62 Moderato

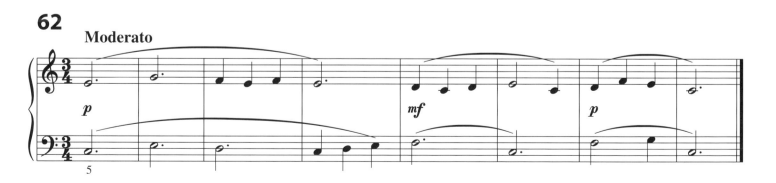

• Scales and different hand positions

You will now need all the notes of the A harmonic minor scale. Play it through with both hands, remembering the G sharp.

Playing scales will also open the way to new hand positions. Play through the scales of C major and G major, noticing how the hand moves over the thumb or the thumb moves under the hand. Can you do this without looking at your fingers?

The following melodies are all in a five-finger hand position, but not necessarily the same as that of the key chord. Check the hand position. (If it is not in the standard hand position you have already learned, a fingering is given for the first note to help you.)

As you read through the melody, also spot where you may need to play a black note (F# or G#).

63

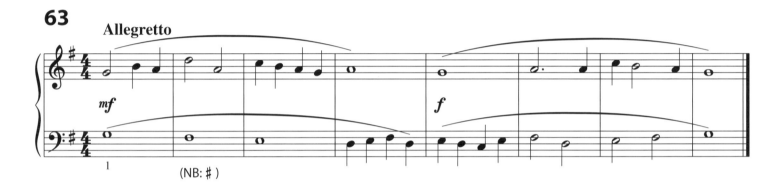

64

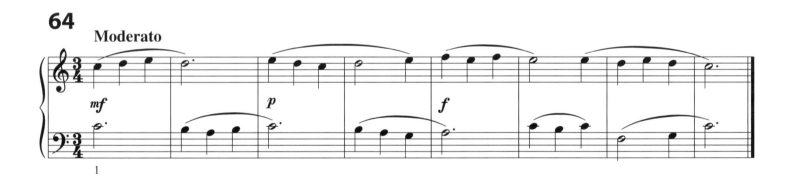

65

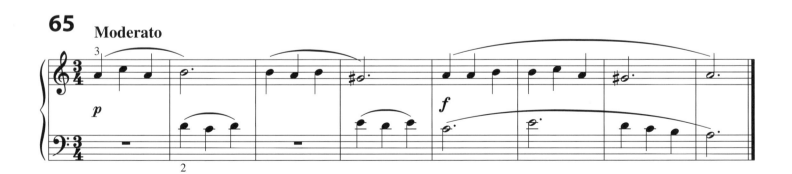

● Moving outside the 5-finger position

As well as using the scale movements to pivot from one hand position to another, you will sometimes need to stretch or contract the hand. Here are some examples of the kind of movement you will need to be able to make.

Practise these movements in the following two pieces. The extensions of the hand are marked with arrows to help you.

66 Moderato

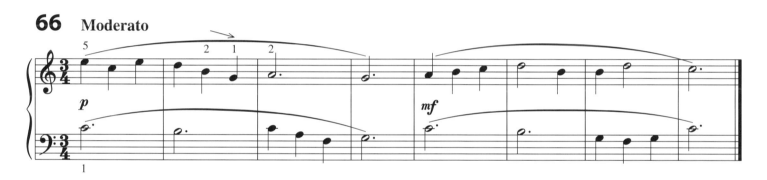

67 Andante

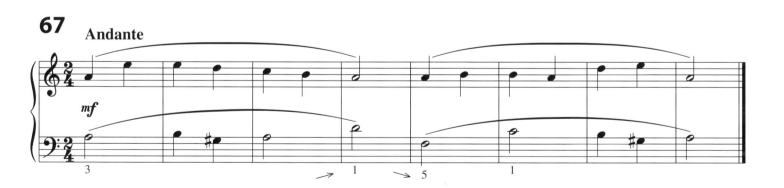

You are now ready to play the pieces on the following pages.

Remember, if the piece is not in the standard hand position you have already learned, a fingering is given for the first note to help you.

68

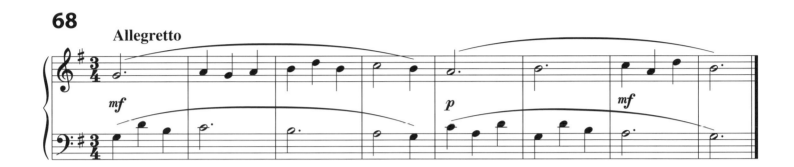

69

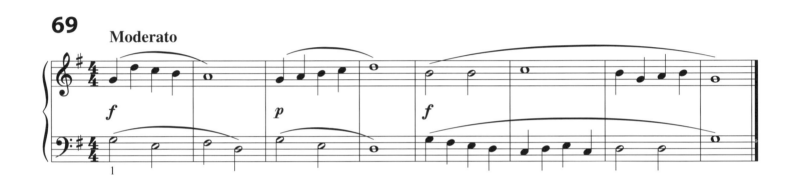

70

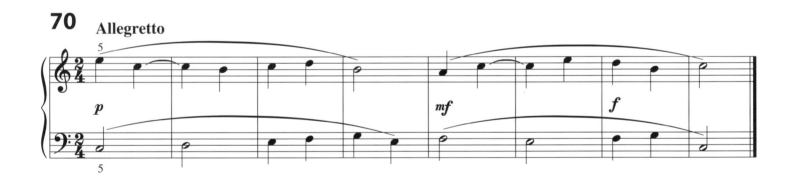

71

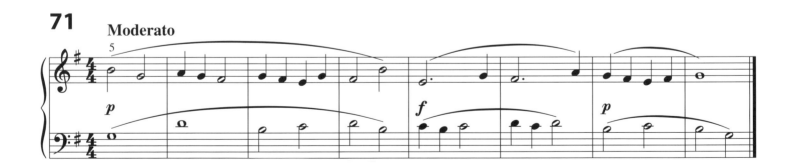

72 Allegretto

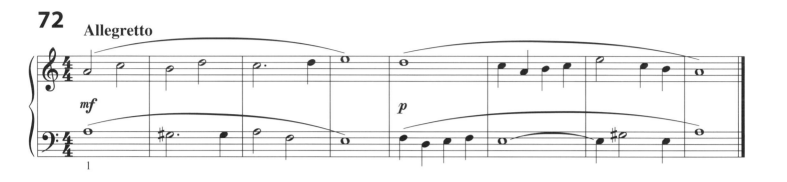

73 Allegretto

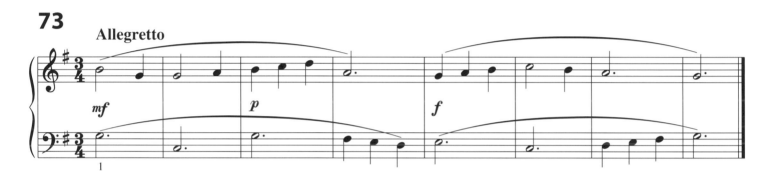

74 Allegretto

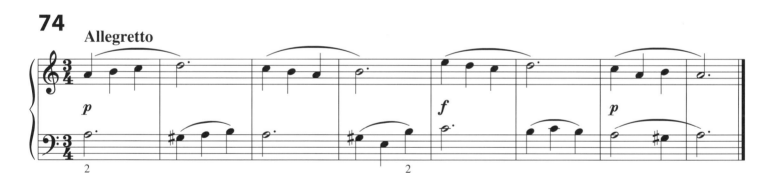

75 Moderato

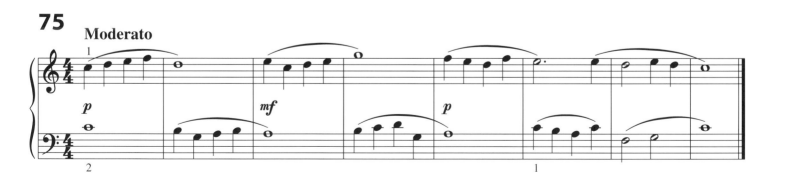

76 Moderato

Did you notice the rest at the start of the left hand?

77 Andante

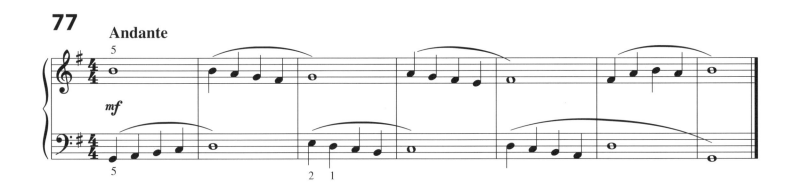

78 Allegretto

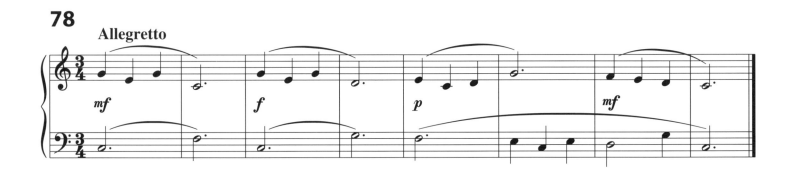

79 Moderato

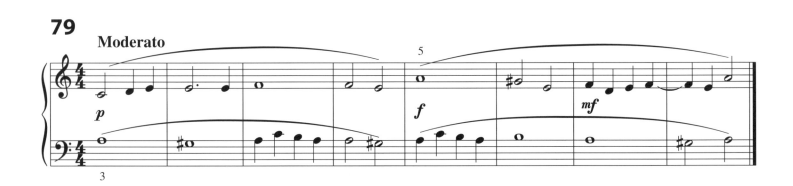

80 Moderato

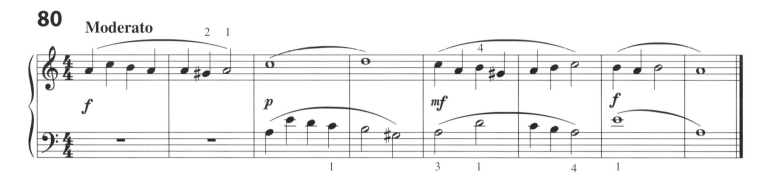

81 Allegretto

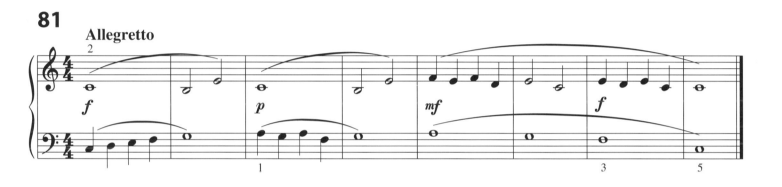

82 Moderato

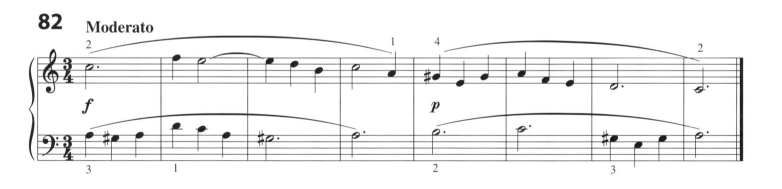

83 Moderato

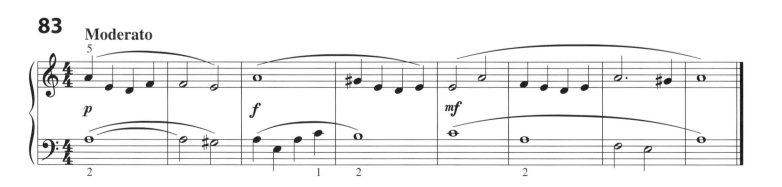

84   Moderato

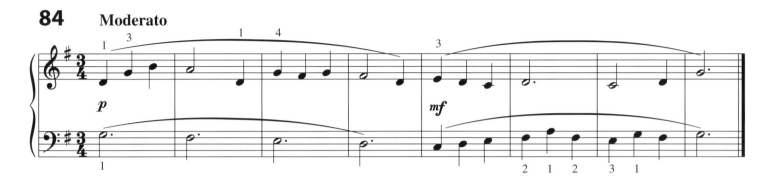

 Melodies 59–84 are of the standard required for Grade 2 examinations.

• Examination preparation

In an examination, you have half a minute to prepare your performance of the sight reading test.

It is important to use this time wisely. First of all, notice the key and time signature. You might play the tonic chord and find the hand position with which you will start the test (look for the highest and lowest notes in each hand). You should certainly make sure that you know if any black notes are needed.

Set the pace securely in your head and read through the test, imagining the sound under your fingers. It might help to sing part of the music or to clap or tap the rhythm but the most important thing is to get a clear idea of what the music will sound like. You can also try out any part of the test if you want to, although it is often a good idea not to do this until you have looked through the piece first.

Have you imagined the effect of the dynamics?

When the examiner asks you to play the piece, play it at the pace you have set. The rhythm is more important than anything else: keep going at all costs! If you make a little slip, do not try to go back and change it—the mistake has already gone. Make sure instead that the next thing is right.

Give a performance of the piece. If you can play the pieces in this book, you will be well prepared for examination sight reading, so enjoy the opportunity to play another piece that you did not know before.